THE STORY OF The Vilna Gaon

THE STORY OF
The Vilna Gaon

SARAH FELDBRAND
ILLUSTRATED BY RACHELI DAVID

ISRAEL BOOKSHOP
Publications

I would like to express my thanks to the staff at Israel Bookshop for their superb work with this book. Thank you to Reb Moshe Kaufman and Mrs. Liron Delmar; the editor, Mrs. Malkie Gendelman; the proofreaders, Mrs. Faige Badian and Mrs. Esther Malky Sonenblick; and the illustrator, Mrs. Racheli David. Thank you as well to Mrs. Malka Millman for her valuable contributions which helped shape this book.

ISBN 978-1-60091-844-5

Distributed by:
Israel Bookshop Publications
501 Prospect Street
Lakewood, NJ 08701
Tel: (732) 901-3009 / Fax: (732) 901-4012
www.israelbookshoppublications.com
info@israelbookshoppublications.com

Printed in Bulgaria

Distributed in Israel by:
Tfutza Publications
P.O.B. 50036
Beitar Illit 90500
972-2-650-9400

Distributed in Europe by:
Lehmanns
Unit E Viking Industrial Park
Rolling Mill Road
Jarrow, Tyne & Wear NE32 3DP
44-191-430-0333

Distributed in Australia by:
Gold's Book and Gift Company
3-13 William Street
Balaclava 3183
613-9527-8775

Distributed in South Africa by:
Kollel Bookshop
Northfield Centre
17 Northfield Avenue
Glenhazel 2192
27-11-440-6679

CHAPTER ONE

An Extraordinary Child

The day had started with a gentle breeze, but as the clouds rose, the wind began to blow fiercely. A young woman was about to cross the bridge over the Romanova river. The bridge was a high one, and the river below it was very deep. In her arms the woman clutched a pillow on which lay a sleeping baby, wrapped tightly in a white blanket.

Suddenly a huge gust of wind threw the woman against the bridge's railing, and the pillow that held her baby daughter fell from her arms, into the river. "My child!" shouted the helpless mother.

The people on the bridge who had seen the accident looked down. All they saw was the

dark rushing river beneath them. There was no sign of the baby. The desperate mother screamed frantic words of prayer, begging Hashem to save her daughter, her treasure. No one dared jump into the roaring waters, for how would they find the child there? Suddenly, something flashed between the waves. It was a pillow floating to the surface, and on it was the infant!

A cry of joy burst forth from the crowd. Miraculously the pillow was stopped by a huge boulder. In an instant, some Jewish men on the shore jumped into the freezing water and, as they all held on to one another, one of them reached for the pillow.

"The child is alive!" the rescuer called out.

"Come to my house," a woman in a nearby house said to the shaking young mother. "I live right here. We can warm the baby up." Carefully the mother lay her shivering little daughter near the stove. But instead of quieting down, the baby's wailing

suddenly increased! It seemed that she had been placed too close to the coals, and her feet had gotten badly burned.

"Water! Water!" came the desperate cry from the mother.

Water was quickly brought, and the baby was bathed to soothe her burns. After a while, the little girl's sobbing slowed down. She grew quieter and quieter until it was clear that she was no longer in pain.

The baby girl, whose name was Treina, had been saved twice that day: first from the water, and then from the fire. It was a double miracle that the people of the village of Sletz would talk about for many years to come, especially when, after Treina grew up, she merited to marry a young Torah scholar by the name of Rav Shlomo Zalman. Treina and her husband were to become the parents of the great *gaon* and holy man, Rabbeinu Eliyahu of Vilna, known as the Vilna Gaon.

Eliyahu was their oldest son, born on the first day of Pesach 5480 (1720). Even when Eliyahu was still a small child, people realized that he was extremely bright. He knew so much at such a young age, absorbing information like a sponge, and he understood everything that anyone told him.

In those days, on the second day of Shavuos, the *rabbanim* and *talmidei chachamim* would gather in shul to celebrate. Fathers and sons of all ages also came to join the celebration. The *rabbanim* would throw out all types of Torah questions for the children to answer. Whoever gave the right answer would be brought into the middle of the circle, and the *rav* who had asked the question would dance with him on his shoulders.

During one such celebration, a *talmid chacham* turned to the children and asked, "Who can tell me where in the Torah Avraham's name is mentioned twice, aside from the *Akeidah* where his name is called out twice?"

While the others were still thinking, Eliyahu burst out, "In *Parshas Toldos* it says, *And these are the generations of Yitzchak, son of Avraham; Avraham was the father of Yitzchak.*" All eyes turned to the young child who had replied without even taking a minute to think.

Then another question was thrown at the audience: "Where in the Torah is there a *pasuk* of eight words, all of which end with a final *mem*?" Again, before the others could even start to think, the high, thin voice of little Eliyahu was heard. To their amazement, his answer was correct, just as before. "There is a *pasuk* in *Vayishlach* which has eight words all ending with the letter *mem: Izim masayim, u'teyashim esrim...*"

Everyone was astonished at the child's knowledge.

"I see that you know what you learned very well. Perhaps you can tell me where there is a *pasuk* with five two-letter words in a row?" another *talmid chacham* asked.

After a moment of thought, Eliyahu had the answer. "There are three such *pesukim*. One is in *Bereishis*, where it says, *Vayoled **Noach es Shem es Cham***. The second one is in *Vayishlach*, where it says, *Al tiri **ki gam zeh lach ben***. And the third one is in *Beshalach*, where it says, ***Ki yad al kes Kah***." The questioner was so excited by the three correct replies of the little boy, that he grabbed Eliyahu and joyfully swung him upon his shoulders and began dancing with him. Soon many others joined, forming a giant happy circle.

When they were tired of dancing, the questions continued, but now they got harder and harder. Each time Eliyahu immediately gave the correct answer. It was clear that he knew the entire Tanach by heart. The amazement of the crowd increased. More than once, Eliyahu was swung upon a man's shoulders, with everyone joining hands around them. This was how the city of Vilna became aware of how very special this child was.

Although Eliyahu learned in a local *cheder*, by the time he was six the *melamed* had nothing more that he could teach him. His father decided that he would become Eliyahu's teacher. Before his sixth birthday, while other children played soldier or threw tops, Eliyahu started learning Gemara. He never joined wrestling games where two boys sat piggyback on other boys and tried to pull each other down, because, as he explained, "I cannot pull down a friend." He kept away from seesaws for a similar reason: "I don't want to be the cause of a friend plopping down each time I go up."

When Eliyahu was six and a half years old, his father taught him a very complicated piece of Gemara. Most adults would have found it difficult to understand, as to do so one had to remember various other pieces of Gemara from many different places, and then fit all those pieces together into one idea. It was something like a difficult puzzle, only much harder. If one didn't fit every idea into

its correct place, the whole picture would become spoiled; if one forgot just one part, he could become all mixed up. Eliyahu's father wanted him to repeat this piece of Gemara so that the city's *rav* and the many Torah scholars who studied with him might hear the way the child explained it.

Eliyahu was not afraid. He walked to the front of the shul and turned to face the scholars who sat waiting. From the yard came the voices of the other boys his age playing games, but Eliyahu heard nothing. He stood straight and tall and repeated what he had prepared, without any mistakes. He spoke so easily and clearly, you might have thought he was speaking about the weather outside! When he finished, a murmur of admiration moved through the room. Many of the scholars rushed to Eliyahu's father to praise the child who had such extraordinary talents.

The group of scholars couldn't stop talking about the child. But one person said, "He did a great job, but I find it hard to believe that he understood everything that he was saying."

"It's true," said another person. "Clearly the boy has an exceptional memory, but who is to say that he can put together something like this on his own?"

The *rav*, Rav Heschel, tried to put an end to the discussion. "I am sure Eliyahu understands what he learns and could do the same thing on his own all over again."

"How could you assume that?" a visiting *rav* asked. "Remember, he is only a child!"

"There is an easy way to find out," Rav Heschel replied. He turned to the child. "I am going to ask you three difficult questions. Take this Gemara into the next room and try to see if you can find the answers."

It didn't take long for the child to emerge from the room with all the right answers, and even some ideas of his own that he'd added. All listened in silence. When he finished, they jumped to their feet

and rushed to hug and kiss him. Now they knew that Rav Heschel was correct: This child was one of a kind.

When the son of the great Rav Dovid Katzenellenbogen visited Vilna and heard about Eliyahu, he begged Rav Shlomo Zalman to let him take the boy back home with him to Rav Dovid. "I think that my father would be very interested in teaching your Eliyahu," he said.

Rav Shlomo Zalman was happy for Eliyahu to have such a special teacher. Indeed, Eliyahu was very pleased to study under Rav Dovid. But after teaching the unbelievable child for a few months, Rav David no longer considered the seven-year-old a student; the boy had reached a level where he could study all parts of the Torah on his own!

By the age of eight, having already mastered Tanach and Gemara, Eliyahu set aside a few hours a day to study the secrets of the Torah, known as Kabbalah. Only a few great scholars in each

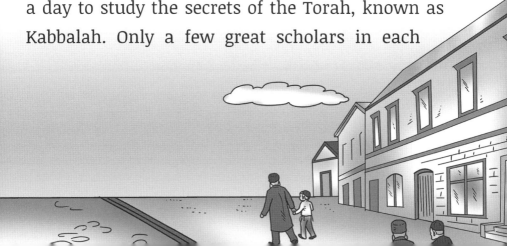

generation know enough to understand this part of the Torah.

While he ate, he studied astronomy. Some astronomers had put together models of the planets. When it was shown to Eliyahu, the young child immediately pointed out mistakes that the scientists had made.

Eliyahu's days revolved around the study of Torah. He would often set learning goals for himself that had to be met by a certain time, in order to push himself to study more and more. At the age of eleven he undertook to complete the study of two Gemaras before the next Simchas Torah. But he was so busy with his other studies that when Simchas Torah arrived, he hadn't even begun either of those Gemaras.

That didn't pose a problem for the young *illui*. Toward evening, as everyone else in the city danced and sang in honor of the Torah, Eliyahu took a volume of the Gemara *Menachos* in his hands and began learning. Later that night, after the Yom Tov meal, he went right back to his studies.

Rav Shlomo Zalman and his family were hosting an important guest that Simchas Torah, Rav Michel, the *rav* of Danavi. The guest noticed the child take a new Gemara in his hands and begin learning it for the first time, but he never dreamed that the boy intended to finish that Gemara—as well as another one!—before the end of Yom Tov.

In the middle of the night Rav Michel woke up. He could hear the voice of young Eliyahu rise and fall as the boy studied more and more of *Menachos*. The guest put on his robe and tiptoed over to the hardworking boy. He stood behind him and noticed how fast he was turning the pages. Had the child actually learned *fifty pages* of Gemara in the past couple of hours?

Rav Michel tapped Eliyahu on the shoulder. "That's no way to study Gemara," he told him. "Even great *talmidei chachamim* need a lot more time

than that to learn fifty pages! Let me ask you some questions to see how much you remember of what you just learned."

Rav Michel asked the boy a question. Immediately Eliyahu responded with the right answer. Rav Michel asked more questions, each one harder than the one before it, but again and again Eliyahu gave him the correct answer. Soon Rav Michel was smiling.

"I was wrong," he said. "You have really learned well. It is late now. I am going back to sleep. Good Yom Tov." He left the boy to his learning and went back to bed.

When Rav Michel awoke to start his day, the stars were still shining in the sky, but the darkness of the night was fading. He washed his hands and went looking for Eliyahu. The boy was still learning. He had finished one Gemara and was halfway through the next. Rav Michel quizzed the boy again and again. Eliyahu was always ready with an answer.

"You don't need me or anyone else to test you. I'll leave you to your studies," said Rav Michel.

A few hours later, Eliyahu had finished the second Gemara, just as he had promised himself. Finally Eliyahu got up. He sang and danced in honor of the Torah, together with all the other Jews of Vilna.

• • •

Eliyahu continued to study one Gemara after another. Even though he already knew more than most *talmidei chachamim* in his generation, he did not slow down. To stay awake through the night, he would take off his shoes and socks and put his bare feet into a pail of icy water.

Before he was thirteen, he knew so much of the secret parts of the Torah that he began making a *golem*. A *golem* is a very strong creature that looks like a man and could move like a man. It is powered by the Name of Hashem in its mouth. Only very great *rabbanim* who knew the secrets of the Torah very well could make a *golem*. In the middle of his work Eliyahu was shown by Heaven that he should stop what he was doing, and so of course he stopped.

By the time he was bar mitzvah, Eliyahu knew more than many famous rabbis. He continued learning without stop, sleeping very little. He ate two meals a day (one in the morning and one at night), each consisting of just two slices of dry bread soaked in water.

The years went by, and people began calling him a *gaon*, which is a title used to describe tzaddikim who lived hundreds of years ago, when Torah scholars knew so much more than they did in more recent times.

The Gaon was about twenty when he married. His wife, Channah, did all that she could to make sure her husband was able to study Torah. As more and more people heard about him, streams of visitors came knocking on his door. He would often slip away and go to a little hut in the forest, where he'd be able to learn in peace. At these times no one but his wife knew where he was. She would bring him food and drink, but she would never tell anyone else where he had gone.

In addition to his Torah studies, the Gaon also became an expert in the sciences. When he began to study the practical side of medicine, his father advised that he stop. "If you become a doctor, people will be constantly begging you to heal them, which will take away precious time from learning Torah."

CHAPTER TWO

In Exile

T he Gaon and his wife were blessed with two
sons, Shlomo Zalman and Yehudah Leib. But
when the family was still young, the Gaon
decided that it was important for him to leave home
and go wandering around from place to place.

At first Channah was not happy about this. "Is
it my fault?" she asked. "I thought I was being so
careful to make sure that no one would disturb your
learning..."

The Gaon shook his head. "No, Channah, it is not
your fault at all. I am grateful to you for all you do,
but there are many reasons why I feel I must leave
home for some time. Here at home I am receiving

too much honor from people. The suffering I will go through as I travel from place to place will make me into a better, more patient person."

Channah tried to smile. She knew that her husband was a very great man, and she trusted what he told her.

"There is another reason why I must go," the Gaon added. "I have studied all the *sefarim* in the city of Vilna, and I have found many mistakes in them. I will try to find other, hopefully older, copies in the big libraries of other cities. Then I will be able to correct the mistakes."

Indeed, one of the most important things the Gaon did for the Jewish people was to correct many errors that had crept into *sefarim* over the years. *Sefarim* were full of mistakes, because for a very long time they'd been copied by hand.

There were no trains or busses in those days, and no smooth highways to travel along, either. Instead, people traveled by horse-drawn wagons across the

bumpy roads. When it was hot and dry outside, clouds of dust would rise from the wagons' wheels and the horses' hoofs, making everyone cough. When it rained, the roads became dirty puddles. Still, this was better than having to walk from place to place.

But the young Gaon did not even own a wagon. Traveling for him meant walking from one city to another, perhaps occasionally getting a ride with someone else, and somehow trying to find places to sleep and food to eat. For years this was exactly what the Gaon did.

He would enter a town and go straight to the *beis midrash* to learn. A day or two later he would be gone, already on his way to the next town's *beis midrash*.

Wherever he went he was determined to hide his knowledge. He did not want anyone to know who he was. He never stayed in any place longer than a day or two, so that he could keep his knowledge a secret.

If his identity was ever discovered, he would quickly leave that town, even if he had just arrived there.

When it did happen, during the course of a conversation, that a *rav* became aware of the Gaon's Torah genius, the *rav* would present him with questions he had that he was unable to answer. The *rav* would be overjoyed when Rav Eliyahu was able to give him the right answers.

In those days many people wandered around from town to town. Most were beggars in need of *tzedakah*. Others were looking for adventure, and a very small amount were like the Gaon: learned people who were hidden tzaddikim. The Gaon learned a lot from the holy men whom he met along his travels.

His experiences with the wandering beggars, though, were not always the most pleasant ones.

"Who is he?" the Gaon heard one bedraggled beggar ask his toothless friend, as they stood in the narrow hallway outside the main shul.

The Gaon, who had already *davened* with the early *minyan*, was just waiting for *davening* to be over so he could enter the shul and begin his learning. But the ragtag band of wandering beggars thought the stranger in their midst was there for another reason: to beg for money, like them.

"That man? He's a nobody," said the toothless beggar. Then he narrowed his eyes as he looked at the Gaon. "But if he gets so much as a single coin before the rest of us do, he's gonna be even less of a nobody than he is now!"

"Taking food out of our mouths when all we're doing is trying to make a living!" the first beggar hissed in self-righteous agreement. "As if towns can afford to give *tzedakah* to every beggar who comes their way!"

"The nerve," a third beggar threw in, glaring hard at the Gaon.

Noting the unwelcome looks he was getting from so many of the beggars, the Gaon realized that the beggars' fear of being cut out of the funds that they

had come to collect was very real. He melted back through the group and only reentered the shul after the beggars were long gone, so as not to upset them any more than he already had.

Sometimes the Gaon's travels caused him to be caught in terrible storms. The clouds would thicken, and all the birds would fly to the safety of their nests, the animals scampering to their burrows underground...but the Gaon would have nowhere to go for shelter. He learned what it meant to suffer from being cold and wet and hungry.

One day Rav Eliyahu paid a wagon driver extra money to stop and wait each time he needed to *daven Shemoneh Esrei.*

"Payment or not," the wagon driver said, after pocketing Rav Eliyahu's extra coin, "I'm not waiting all day for you."

"It won't be that long," the Gaon assured him.

Later that day, when it was time for Minchah, Rav Eliyahu asked the wagon driver to please stop.

"It is not right, wasting time like this," the wagon driver grumbled, but he pulled the horses to a stop. "You know, others said their prayers in the wagon. I don't understand why you can't do the same."

The Gaon was already too deep into his prayers to answer.

When he finished *Shemoneh Esrei*, he took his three steps back and looked around. The wagon driver was long gone...and so was his bundle that he had left in the back of the wagon. The Gaon was left with nothing more than the clothes on his back. He had no food and no money. Weak from lack of food, as he hadn't eaten all day, the Gaon simply walked back to the main road and continued his trip by foot.

He was not distressed by such matters. The only thing that would upset him was when he could not keep the mitzvos as he would have wished.

One Ta'anis Esther the Gaon found himself in the country of Prussia (now Germany). The hours were

passing, and the Gaon was far from any Jewish settlement. The sun would soon set. How would he find a *minyan* of Jews so he could hear the Megillah properly? Just then, a wagon came out of the forest behind him. The Gaon hurried toward it, noticing that the wagon was piled high with pots and jugs.

"Can you take me to a town with a Jewish community?" the Gaon asked the driver. "I will pay you well for your trouble."

When the man hesitated, the Gaon took out a coin and held it up to the light.

The peasant driver smiled. "All right. Get in, but be careful not to let any of the jugs fall."

The Gaon climbed onto the back of the wagon, and the driver continued his journey. By now the sun had already sank down to the horizon, and a gray darkness was spreading all over the sky. "Do we still have far to go?" asked the Gaon.

The peasant didn't turn around. "About a mile or two."

Suddenly there was a huge bump in the road. "Hold on to the jugs!" cried the man.

But the next moment the Gaon found himself on the ground, hurt and bleeding, surrounded by hundreds of pieces of broken clay.

The wagon driver was furious at the loss of his jugs. "You fool, why couldn't you hold on tighter to the jugs? Now they are smashed, and it will cost me hundreds of *gulden*!" He was still holding the horsewhip, and he struck the Gaon with it across the chest.

Without reacting, the Gaon took hold of his bundle and hurried away. The driver ran after him for a while before turning back to his wagon. The Gaon sped down the darkening road, his chest burning with pain. But his only concern was that he reach the Jewish community in time to hear Megillah with a *minyan*.

Finally the Gaon found a Jewish man. "*A freilichen Purim!*" he called out to him. "Could you please direct me to the shul?"

The Jew looked curiously at the Gaon. "It's that way—the tall building up ahead."

The Gaon hurried to the shul, only to hear that he had missed the Megillah *leining*. He found some older boys outside. "I haven't yet *leined* the Megillah. Could you come in to make a *minyan* for me?" he pleaded with them.

"We just heard the Megillah, and we'll be hearing it again tomorrow morning. Why would we want to hear it yet a third time?" they nastily replied.

"I'll pay you," the Gaon said. "Look, I will give you two gold coins."

"All right," the boys replied, "but only if you pay us in advance."

"Certainly," said the Gaon.

The Gaon gave them the money, made the *brachos*, and began to *lein*. But to his distress, the boys only laughed and left the shul. The Gaon had to continue the Megillah alone.

Years later, when the Gaon told over this

story, he cried with sorrow over having to *lein* the Megillah without a *minyan*.

• • •

Pesach had almost arrived, and Rav Eliyahu, who was extremely careful about what he ate, needed a place to stay for Yom Tov. He made his way to the home of the *rav* of Zalkava, Rav Mordechai Zev, and knocked on his door.

"How can I help you, my son?" Rav Mordechai Zev asked when he opened the door.

"I am a visitor in town, and I'm wondering if I could spend Pesach with you."

Rav Mordechai Zev opened his eyes wide in surprise. "Why would you pick my house? Surely, there are richer men in the city who would provide you with better food and lodgings than I can give you."

"The *rav* knows that the laws of Pesach are very strict. Not all the people know them well. I am certain that you keep all the laws in the proper way. Your

matzah was surely guarded very, very carefully, and all the things you will use for the Seder will be just as the Torah tells us they should be."

Pleased with his answer, the *rav* said, "I am very happy to welcome you. Stay with us for Pesach and for as long as you wish afterward."

Rav Mordechai Zev watched in surprise as his guest arranged his Seder plate. He used only two matzos instead of three, and arranged the items on the plate differently. (There is another opinion that holds this way, and Rav Eliyahu followed that opinion.) Rav Mordechai Zev did not say anything, but as the Seder continued and his guest made some more changes, he became more and more displeased. *It's not right that such a young man should be doing things so differently from the rest of the Jewish community*, he thought.

The next morning, the *rav* consulted with the other *rabbanim* of the city regarding what had happened. "I hesitated to say anything to my guest,

because there is something so special about him," he explained. "But perhaps I am wrong."

One of the *rabbanim* suggested, "See how learned he is. If he is not a Torah scholar, we will have to do something about this."

At the noon *seudah*, Rav Mordechai Zev turned to his young guest and asked, "Would you honor me with some words of Torah?"

Rav Eliyahu remained silent.

"Just a few words," Rav Mordechai Zev pleaded. When he saw that his guest was not responding, he said, "I will tell you some of my own Torah thoughts, and maybe you will have something to say about them."

Rav Mordechai Zev spoke at length. When he finished and still Rav Eliyahu was quiet, the *rav* said, "Perhaps my *divrei Torah* were too difficult for you to follow. I am ready to repeat everything to you, so that you can understand and share your opinion about what I said."

Rav Eliyahu saw that he had no choice but to respond. "That is not necessary," he said, and began fluently repeating the entire discussion. He then shared many other deep and complicated *divrei Torah* on the topic.

He is a great man, thought the *rav, a rare genius who seems to know all the treasures of the Torah.*

From that moment on, the *rav* and the people of the community could not stop showing their respect for their special visitor. Knowing that he would be leaving after Yom Tov, they planned a grand feast in his honor. But the Gaon rose early the day after Yom Tov and left the city while everyone was still asleep. On his pillow he left a piece of paper on which he had written down the cost of all the food he had eaten, as well as the money to pay for it. He much preferred to give than to take.

• • •

During the time that he was traveling, the Gaon once arrived at a village inn. The inn sat on top

of a hill from which you could see the rest of the village, as well as the surrounding towns, orchards, and fields. All of it belonged to the local landowner, called a *poritz*.

The owner of the inn, a warm-hearted Jew named Feivish, was very welcoming. "Please come in, honored guest!" he called out when he saw Rav Eliyahu. He didn't know who the visitor was, but he could tell by looking at him that he was special.

"I see that you are a scholar. I will ask my wife to prepare a bed in the best room for you."

The room was bright and airy. The walls were newly whitewashed, and the bedding was fresh. The Gaon thanked his host and settled himself in. Then he opened his Gemara and began to learn.

He did not hear the sound of hoofbeats approaching the inn, nor did he hear the raised voices in the room below. The *poritz* had unexpectedly arrived at the inn.

The *poritz's* servant banged on the front door and called out, "Feivish!"

The innkeeper hurried to open the door. His face was pale. "Sir, I wasn't expecting you until tomorrow."

"Well, we are here today," the servant replied.

The *poritz* entered the inn, pulled off his gloves, and tucked them into his belt. "Just bring the horses around and prepare my room for me!" he ordered.

"Your...room." Feivish swallowed hard. "Yes."

The room that the Gaon was sleeping in was actually the *poritz's* room. It was supposed to be reserved for him and ready any time he arrived. But for years he had only come on market days. What should Feivish do? He knew that the *poritz* could take away his inn if he would get angry at him, and then Feivish would be left without any *parnassah*. On the other hand, how could he embarrass a Torah scholar by asking him to leave his room?

Feivish made his decision. He would not let the great mitzvah of honoring a Torah scholar slip through his hands. He would trust in Hashem and hope that the *poritz* would understand.

"I'm sorry, sir," Feivish said, "but your room has been taken."

"Taken?!" the *poritz* shouted in a combination of amazement and anger. "Taken?!" he repeated.

Feivish tried to explain. "A great scholar came to the inn..." he began.

"So get rid of the fellow immediately!" the *poritz* interrupted.

"Most honored sir, had I known that you were coming, I would have kept the room free for you, but now that he's already settled in the room..."

Behind him the door opened a crack, and he could hear his wife's warning voice. "Feivish..."

The *poritz* did not let him continue. "If you will not tell him to leave, I will throw him out myself, and I will make you sorry you ever set eyes on me. Not only will I fire you, but I will make sure you never find any work again!"

The *poritz* pounded up the stairs and threw open the door to the Gaon's room.

Suddenly his anger disappeared. It was replaced by fear and trembling. "I...beg your pardon," he said to the Gaon, and the *poritz* gently shut the door.

Feivish and his wife heard the *poritz's* steps, hesitant and soft, coming back down the steps. "Your guest is truly a holy man," the *poritz* said. "It is an honor for me to have him in my room."

• • •

On one of the Gaon's journeys between cities, the wagon driver, a Jewish man, fell asleep, and the horses turned into a field, where they began nibbling on some vegetables there. The owner of the field, a strong, non-Jewish farmer, came running toward the wagon. He reached the back of the wagon where the Gaon was sitting and slapped him hard. "Jew! Look what you did to my vegetables!"

Although the Gaon could have replied, "I didn't do anything! It's the wagon driver's fault," he didn't do so, as it is forbidden to speak badly about a fellow Jew. Instead he accepted the beating in silence.

• • •

In every Jewish community that the Gaon visited, he would examine the *sefarim* there, paying careful attention to the older ones. He visited libraries of *rabbanim* who had many *sefarim*. As he expected, he found many small but important differences between these old *sefarim* and the ones he knew from back home in Vilna.

• • •

During his travels, the Gaon learned many important lessons. One Thursday evening he arrived at a small town. It was cold and windy outside, and the shutters of the shul rattled loudly. But the Gaon, who had taken out a Gemara and immersed himself in his learning, heard and felt nothing.

In the morning the *shamash* arrived and lit coals in the black, cast-iron stove at the back of the shul. This provided the room with a bit of heat.

After *davening*, all the men removed their *tefillin* and *talleisim* and hurried out into the chilly air to

begin their day's work. All, that is, except for the Gaon and one old, blind man who stayed behind.

Soon enough the old man's wife entered the *beis midrash* with some food that she had brought for her husband.

"Before I wash and eat, I want you to do something for me," the man said to his wife. "There is a stranger learning here in the *beis midrash*; I keep hearing his voice. I would like you to invite him to eat with me, for I am sure that he is a scholar and a special person."

She looked to where he had pointed. "I see him. He is quite young. Wait, and I will go and speak to him."

She walked over to Rav Eliyahu. "My husband asks that you please join him for breakfast," she said.

Rav Eliyahu rose and made his way to the old man. "Thank you for the invitation, but I really can't eat with you."

The old man understood why Rav Eliyahu would not join him. "Please do not refuse me," he replied. "Fortunately Hashem has given me and my wife more than enough for ourselves; we have plenty to give to others."

"How do you have so much food?" asked Rav Eliyahu.

"Every day my wife goes to the mill where the grains of wheat are ground into flour. She has the miller's permission to gather the dust from the grain that falls to the floor. *Baruch Hashem* this wheat dust gives us all that we need to eat, and we can even support other poor people."

Hearing this, the Gaon agreed to eat with the old man. He sat down beside him, and the man's wife brought him a tin bowl filled with what looked like thick, steaming farina.

Later, the old man approached the Gaon and said, "You must come and spend Shabbos together with me."

"Thank you so much," said the Gaon, "but why should I trouble you? I am sure that someone else will invite me, so you need not worry."

The blind man was insistent. "Please don't refuse. We have plenty of everything—we really do! On Shabbos we live like rich people and have many guests."

"But how do you manage?"

"Every Friday my wife goes to the slaughterhouse. She helps the women there pluck the feathers from the chickens. For her work she gets the feet and heads of the chickens, and she makes all sorts of dishes from them. With that and the wheat dust, we have a great deal of good food."

Rav Eliyahu smiled and accepted the invitation.

After *davening* Rav Eliyahu accompanied the blind man home. The table was set for many people. At each place stood two small *challos*. The blind man stood at the door and greeted all of his guests, his face shining with happiness.

Many of the guests were Torah scholars, and much Torah was discussed in between the *zemiros*. The blind man did what he could to make his guests happy, but he was clearly the happiest of them all.

Years later the Gaon would repeat this story because of its important lesson. "From that old man and his wife, I learned that a person can be poor and have little, but he can still be very happy."

• • •

By the time the Gaon reached Lissa in Germany, he could no longer keep his identity a secret. One community after another began hearing stories about the great Gaon who was traveling around from city to city. When Rav Yaakov Tzvi of Berlin received a letter informing him that the great Gaon would soon be arriving in his community, he sent the following message to the man who collected the tolls on the bridge into Berlin: "When a man named Eliyahu arrives, inform me as quickly as you can,

for I wish to bring him to my home." Rav Yaakov Tzvi also informed all the *talmidei chachamim* of Berlin that the Gaon would soon be their guest.

Rav Yaakov Tzvi's neighbor, a professor who was the head of the local non-Jewish university, heard about the upcoming visit of this remarkable rabbi. "Why is everyone so excited about this particular rabbi?" he asked Rav Yaakov Tzvi.

"This rabbi is famous for knowing the entire Torah!" the neighbor was told. "He is also familiar with all of the sciences in the world. Additionally, he is a very holy man."

"Interesting," the neighbor replied, and he returned to his house down the road.

The Gaon was received with great honor at the home of Rav Yaakov Tzvi. The next morning, there was a knock on the door. It was the professor who lived down the street.

"You told me that your visiting rabbi is a great scientist. We have a question on astronomy that

we have been trying to figure out for years. Perhaps your rabbi can help us?"

"Please wait here while I ask if he can see you," Rav Yaakov Tzvi said.

He told the Gaon about his neighbor's request. "I think that if you agree to answer his question, it will be a big *kiddush Hashem*," Rav Yaakov Tzvi added. "The non-Jews will have more respect for Torah scholars." The Gaon agreed.

As the professor presented his question, the Gaon drew some diagrams on a piece of paper. When the professor stopped talking, the Gaon used the drawings to explain his answer. The professor stood there in amazement.

"That answer makes so much sense!" he exclaimed, his whole body trembling with excitement. "The greatest minds in Berlin have been working on this question for years, without success—yet you figured out an answer in just moments!"

The professor shared the Gaon's answer with the other scientists. They, too, were astounded, and they all wanted to meet the Gaon themselves. The professor sent a message to Rav Yaakov Tzvi, telling him of their request.

"You are too late," Rav Yaakov Tzvi replied. "The rabbi is no longer in Berlin. While I was still sleeping last night, he left the city."

CHAPTER THREE

Return to Vilna

Early one morning, many years after the Gaon had left Vilna, a wagon appeared in the city. The wagon was no different from many others, but the driver certainly was. The man looked special, while the individual sleeping soundly in the back of the wagon looked anything but.

"Interesting!" said the Jew who was watching the wagon approach. Suddenly he jumped up in surprise, calling out loudly, "Yidden, people of Vilna, the Gaon has returned!"

Someone joined him at his post. "It cannot be!" he said. "The Gaon is no wagon driver!"

But it certainly was the Gaon! When the

people heard the news, they came pouring out of their houses. A huge crowd formed to welcome their treasure back to the city.

Several people shook the man in the back of the wagon awake. He was clearly the wagon driver... and even more clearly, he was not doing his job. The townspeople began yelling at him for his lack of respect for the Gaon.

"The driver is tired; he just wants to rest a bit," the Gaon explained. "Please, let him sleep!"

Confused by the noise and the crowd, the driver groggily sat up. He wiped the sleep from his eyes and asked, "What is going on here?"

"Do you know who has been driving your wagon?" the people scolded him. "How could you let the holy Gaon of Vilna take over for you?"

The driver turned pale. "What?! The Gaon of Vilna?!" Ashamed, he quickly jumped out of the wagon and fell at the Gaon's feet. "Please forgive me, Rebbi! I didn't know!"

"You have nothing to worry about," the Gaon smilingly replied. Then he blessed him: "May Hashem give you much *parnassah*, easily and honestly."

The Gaon's wife, Channah, and their children were overjoyed to see him. It had been difficult for Channah to manage the children alone, but she had tried comforting herself with the knowledge that her husband was adding to his Torah knowledge and becoming an even greater and holier person.

She wasn't the only one who had been waiting impatiently for the Gaon to return. The entire community of Vilna had been, too.

The Gaon moved into the apartment where he would live for the rest of his life, just off the shul's front yard. His apartment was surrounded by an entire complex of shuls. In one, the *beis din* met to make important decisions. Sometimes the *beis din* had to punish people who had done something wrong. There was a prison cell where these people

were kept until it was decided what would happen to them. Between two shuls was a place where meat was slaughtered. Across from it was a large room with beds, where up to twenty visitors could sleep and, if they were ill, could be cared for. More than one *cheder* used rooms in the shuls, and there was a public bathhouse in the back of the whole complex. Also, this complex of shuls was the only place where the Jews of Vilna could get water (it was brought to the courtyard through wooden pipes).

Because so many things were happening around this courtyard, the place was usually noisy and full of people. But the Gaon heard nothing of the commotion. Fearing that he might become distracted by the noise from outside his apartment, he kept the shutters in his home tightly closed, and studied Torah by the light of a candle.

The Gaon learned alone, all day and night. He would sleep three times during the night, for no more than half an hour each time, even when he was ill. If you were in his room when he slept, you would see his lips moving constantly, and if you moved your ear close to his mouth, you would hear words from different Gemaras being quoted even during his sleep.

"The reason why Hashem created sleep," he would explain, "is so that a person can learn more than he could during the day. When a person is awake, his body has more power, but when he is asleep, his *neshamah* has the upper hand. Many Torah secrets are told to a person in his sleep, when his *neshamah* is free and in control."

When it was time for Shacharis, a *minyan* would gather in his home. After *davening*, the Gaon would eat breakfast and sleep a bit. He would then rise and learn the entire day until Minchah.

Every day the Gaon reviewed a hundred pages of Gemara, and every month he went through the entire *Shas*. During each Yom Tov, he learned the Gemara relating to that holiday, and every Shabbos

he went through *Maseches Shabbos* and *Maseches Eiruvin*, both of which deal with Shabbos.

The Jewish community of Vilna appreciated the great treasure that lived in their midst. They realized how much they all gained from the Gaon's *limud haTorah*, and they did not want him to stop learning. To ensure that he would not have to work or open up a business, they tried to persuade him to become the *rav* of Vilna and earn a *parnassah* like that. But he refused. A *rav* has so many things to take care of, and the Gaon was concerned that the position would take him away from his Torah learning.

The Vilna community then decided to give the Gaon a regular allowance anyway, even without him becoming their *rav*. This would allow him to continue to study in peace. With the money he received, he could pay his rent and buy food and clothing for himself and his children.

Each week the *parnas*, who was the president of the community, would hand the money to the *shamash* to bring to Rav Eliyahu. Before Shabbos and Yamim Tovim, the community would give Rav Eliyahu additional gifts and food, through the same messenger.

This *shamash* was an extremely poor man. In those days, being poor meant hunger and cold and often even illness. One day the *shamash's* wife heard some coins jingling in her husband's pocket.

"What do you have in your pocket?" she asked her husband.

"Nothing," the *shamash* replied.

"Tell me what nothing it is," she insisted.

"It's just some money that I must bring to someone."

"To whom?"

"To the Gaon, Rav Eliyahu," was his reply.

The wife wasn't finished. "Who gave you the money?"

Her husband explained that the money came from the head of the community, and when she

asked how much money it was, he told her that as well.

Upon hearing the amount, she cried out, "So much money, and we have so little! We can't even afford to buy enough food for our family, and our children run around in rags, without shoes. You should take off one coin from the amount you give Rav Eliyahu. You deserve it for being the messenger."

At first her husband wouldn't hear of it, but she refused to let up, bothering her husband about it again and again. A few weeks passed in this way.

One week, when the children had had nothing to eat for a couple of days, the *shamash's* wife begged him especially hard to keep one of Rav Eliyahu's coins.

I will give in to her just this once, he thought, because he could no longer bear her pleading, and he slipped one coin into his own pocket.

When the Gaon saw that part of his pay was missing, he said nothing. He had total trust in

Hashem that He would provide him with everything that he needed.

The *shamash* was sure that he would soon be punished. When he went to shul, he was hardly able to lift his eyes. When the *parnas* looked at him, he felt like thousands of needles were stinging him. Yet the days passed and no one said anything to him about it. It was clear that the Gaon had not told anyone.

The next week, when the *shamash* again received the money to give to the Gaon, his wife was waiting for him. "Do you see? You were worried for nothing. Give me just one coin again today so that i can buy food for our family."

"Absolutely not!" The *shamash* was really frightened. "I will not touch any more of the Gaon's money!"

But his wife's hot tears persuaded him, and once again, feeling guilty and scared, he kept one coin for his own family. When he knocked on the Gaon's door to give him the rest of the money, he couldn't tell which was pounding harder, his hand on the door or his heart.

Once a person lets the *yetzer hara* in, and repeats a sin a few times, it becomes harder and harder for him to do *teshuvah* and stop sinning. By the third week, it wasn't that hard for the *shamash* to take one coin for himself. Soon he was taking two coins... and then three. Before long he was keeping *all* the money for his own family.

The Gaon could have told the *parnas* that he wasn't receiving the money, but he refused to do so, because he knew that it meant that the thief would be punished. Embarrassing a Jew was out of the question. His wife didn't tell anyone, either. She also knew that shaming a person was like killing him.

Channah found ways to buy food, and they continued to suffer in silence.

One day the *shamash* got sick. He asked his children to call the *parnas* to his bedside, and when

the *parnas* arrived, he asked that he close the door behind him.

Then the *shamash* burst out crying. "I have sinned!" he moaned. "I have caused the holy Gaon and his family much sorrow!" His sobs made it difficult for him to continue.

The *parnas* tried to reassure him. "I am sure the Gaon will forgive you for whatever you did. He is a great tzaddik," he said.

"No, I'm sure he won't. *Oy*, who knows if I will ever be able to repair the damage I have done?" the *shamash* sobbed. "If only I could do *teshuvah*!"

"What could you have done that is so terrible?" the *parnas* wondered. "You haven't told me what happened."

The *shamash* wiped away his tears. "I stole; I robbed. You trusted me..." He couldn't continue.

The *parnas* was confused. How had the man stolen and robbed? What had he done? "Speak!" he ordered. "Tell me what you have done."

The *shamash* confessed everything. "For a long time, I have been keeping the money meant for Rav Eliyahu. And even though he knew that I stole his money, he never said anything about it."

The *parnas* was in shock. This news was absolutely terrible. How had the Gaon and his family lived all these years?!

Seeing the pain of the *shamash*, who could not utter another word, the *parnas* advised him, "Send your children to ask Rav Eliyahu to forgive you for being so cruel to him."

"Yes," whispered the *shamash*. "If he forgives me, then perhaps Hashem will forgive me also."

The Gaon was not angry with the *shamash*. He had forgiven him long before. When the *shamash* heard that he was forgiven, he died with a contented look on his face.

• • •

Now that we see how in control the Gaon was

with his thoughts and emotions, do you want to know what *would* really upset him? If he ever forgot a Torah thought, the Gaon would become very distressed. In fact, when the Gaon had trouble understanding a Torah thought, he would worry about it so much that he would become ill.

Rav Chaim Volozhiner was the Gaon's close student. He would visit Vilna once or twice a year, and he always came to the Gaon with a long list of questions that he needed help with. Once, Rav Chaim arrived in Vilna on a Friday morning. Before he even had a chance to visit the Gaon, a messenger came running out to him.

"Rav Chaim! The Gaon is having trouble understanding something, and the question is causing him so much distress that he could hardly eat for the past three days!"

As fast as he could, Rav Chaim went to the Gaon's home. There he found the Gaon's wife and children almost in tears.

"We're so glad to see you," the Gaon's sons said. "Father isn't feeling well. Go inside; you might be able to help him."

Rav Chaim entered the Gaon's room. Rav Eliyahu was sitting over a Gemara, with a huge bandage tied around his head.

"Rebbi! What is the matter?"

"There is a part of this Gemara that I am not able to understand, and it has made me very ill. I have a throbbing headache. Come! Two heads are better than one. Maybe you can help me."

"Rebbi," protested Rav Chaim, "if you can't solve the problem, how do you expect me to be able to do so?"

"Let us try," said the Gaon.

They went over the Gemara together. Suddenly a possible answer flashed into Rav Chaim's mind, and he told it to the Gaon. Immediately, the Gaon smiled. His question was answered. The Gaon's wife brought a tray of food into the room, and finally, the Gaon was able to eat.

• • •

By the time the Gaon turned forty, he had already written about seventy *sefarim*. Many of them were written on the secrets of the Torah. He also wrote a book on *dikduk* (*Lashon Hakodesh* grammar); a book on the geography of Eretz Yisrael; a book on trigonometry, since math is very important in the study of Gemara; and *peirushim* on *Pirkei Avos* and *Mishlei*.

It was at this time that the Gaon decided it was time for him to begin teaching. His two sons became his students, in addition to a group of serious *talmidei chachamim* who gathered around him. He shared with them all the Torah ideas that kept flying into his head, and they wrote down a lot of them. Unfortunately, not everything could be recorded, because the Gaon's mind was constantly churning out Torah thoughts. One day he told his students that he had one hundred and fifty comments on one *pasuk* of *Shir Hashirim*. There just wasn't enough time in the day to record everything.

Only the brightest minds could understand the Gaon. They had to remember every word, even every letter, of what they learned. His students were not allowed to go ahead as they liked, but had to follow the learning program that the Gaon had prepared. After they mastered Tanach, they began to work on the Mishnah. Finally, they would be introduced to the Gemara. His students were all holy people, chosen because of their great fear of Hashem.

CHAPTER FOUR

Devotion to Torah

For fifty years the Gaon slept only a total of two hours daily, as short naps scattered about the night and day (as mentioned previously). The rest of his time was devoted mainly to learning. For forty of those fifty years, he almost never left his room. He reviewed everything he learned hundreds, even thousands, of times. He knew all of our holy *sefarim* as well as we know our name and address. He could tell you how many letters each of them had. He was capable of stating how many times a particular sage was mentioned in each Gemara.

On the Gaon's travels, he had not only studied hard, but had also made the effort to find as many

different copies of *sefarim* as he could. When Hashem sees a tzaddik like the Vilna Gaon, who doesn't stop learning Torah, He gives him special *siyata d'Shmaya*. That means that Hashem actually gifted him with the right understanding of the Torah that he had learned. This made it possible for the Gaon to correct so many mistakes in so many *sefarim*. Torah scholars were very grateful for his corrections; with them, the Torah became easier to understand.

Even though he knew so much Torah that all the Jewish people referred to him by the name "Gaon," a title given to great *talmidei chachamim* from many years before, Rav Eliyahu labored on his studies as if he were a beginner. His students said that his face would change colors as he worked to understand more and more Torah.

If the Gaon felt that he had wasted even a minute, he would mark down the date and time in a notebook so that he wouldn't forget about it. Then, on Erev

Yom Kippur, he would take out the notebook and, with real tears, do *teshuvah* for the time he had wasted. He would confess the sin on Yom Kippur: "For this sin which I have sinned in wasting time from Torah study..." The total never came to more than three hours over the course of the whole year.

The Gaon would say that every Jew should know at least one Gemara by heart, so that he could always study it, even when he did not have a *sefer* in front of him. This was his way, to review and study, study and review, again and again.

One day his great student, Rav Chaim of Volozhin, asked his *rebbi* a question. "I have studied and reviewed *Maseches Shabbos* twenty times, but I still do not feel that I have mastered it. What should I do?"

"Twenty times?!" the Gaon wondered. "You only studied it twenty times? And you expect to know it well? That is not possible."

"Then how many times should one study and review a Gemara, in order to really know it?" asked Rav Chaim.

"*Chazal* tell us that one must review his studies one hundred and one times in order to understand them. After that, you must continue to review to be a true expert. That is how Torah knowledge is acquired."

In his writings, the Gaon quotes Torah thoughts he had heard from Yaakov Avinu, Moshe Rabbeinu, Eliyahu Hanavi, and others. Every night, the Gaon's *neshamah* rose to the Heavenly yeshivah, where he learned with many of our people's great teachers. Even though he only slept for a very short time, he made the most of his sleeping time to learn. Sometimes these tzaddikim from previous generations would come down to Earth while the Gaon was awake, to learn with him then as well.

CHAPTER FIVE

Love of Mitzvos

The Gaon taught that money is given to a person to be used for *tzedakah*. He himself never gave less than a fifth of his money to *tzedakah*.

One day the Gaon received a letter from Rav Yaakov Sofer of Keidan, who had many daughters to marry off and no money. "My first daughter is now ready to get married, and I have no friends or relatives who can help me out with it," he wrote. The Gaon collected the money that was needed, as well as clothing for the girl.

There were many who turned to the Gaon for help. They came to him because it was hard for them to ask others for assistance, but the Gaon seemed so

happy to do the mitzvah. He made the person feel that he was doing the Gaon a favor by allowing him to help the person out!

When there was no way for him to put together money to help someone out, the Gaon would give away his own food or items in the house. He also worked hard to get prisoners out of jail. Usually that too was a matter of money, which he collected wherever he could.

The Gaon wore his *tallis* and *tefillin* all day long. He felt that every man should wear *tefillin* for all of his learning hours, because it is such an important mitzvah. He would explain that when a person wears *tefillin*, he is fulfilling eight positive commandments.

The Gaon loved all the mitzvos so much that he tried keeping even those that only certain people, like farmers, are obligated to keep. One day he asked one of his sons to buy him a tiny piece of land.

"Father, what will you be doing with the land?"

"I will plant a fruit tree."

"A fruit tree?" The son was surprised. He knew that his father only ate bread and water, so why would he need a fruit tree?

"I want to keep the mitzvah of *orlah*, by not eating the fruit that grows on the tree in the first three years. I also would like to keep the mitzvah of *neta revai*, by redeeming the fruit that grows on the tree in the fourth year."

The next year, when the Gaon asked his son to buy him a field of wheat, his son was no longer surprised.

"We will plant wheat, which we will use to make *shmurah matzah* for Pesach," the Gaon said.

The Gaon arranged for the wheat to be guarded. Then, in early spring, he called to his son, "It is time to go cut the wheat!"

What great joy filled him, as he left the uncut stalks at the end of the field for the poor, as is required by the mitzvah of *pei'ah*! His face shone

each time a stalk fell to the ground and he didn't pick it up, leaving it for the poor, as required by the mitzvah of *leket*. And of course he gave a tenth of his wheat to the poor, for the mitzvah of *ma'aser ani*. The Vilna Gaon felt that it was important to keep these mitzvos even during *galus*, and even outside of Eretz Yisrael.

The Gaon badly wanted to keep the mitzvos relating to *kohanim*, too. He bought a calf, had it slaughtered, and then gave a *kohen* the portions which *kohanim* would receive during the times of the Beis Hamikdash. He also made the *brachah* of *Shehecheyanu* on having the chance to do that mitzvah. Although there are reasons why these mitzvos are not kept nowadays, the Vilna Gaon and other great *rabbanim* felt that they do still apply.

Each year as the Yamim Tovim approached, special messengers left Vilna to search for an *esrog* for the Gaon. One year they visited the different places where *esrogim* were known to grow, but

they couldn't find any. It looked like they would be forced to return home without an *esrog*.

The messengers were very upset. Would their holy *rav* not have his own perfect *esrog* this year? The thought was terrible.

On their way back to Vilna, they visited every *esrog* dealer they could find. Finally, they found an *esrog* that they knew would please the Gaon. But to their dismay, the merchant told them, "I'm sorry, but this *esrog* is not for sale. I have decided to keep it for my own use."

"We are ready to pay double the value of the *esrog*!" the messengers told him.

The messenger shook his head. "I told you, it's not for sale."

"What if we pay you *triple* its value?"

"You don't seem to understand. I am not ready to give away this mitzvah for money," the merchant said.

"Look, this is very important," the Gaon's messengers said. "We need that *esrog*. What if we

pay you five or six times as much as the *esrog's* value?"

"Who is this *esrog* for?" the merchant asked.

At first the messengers did not want to say. But finally they told him, "It's for the Gaon of Vilna."

As soon as the merchant heard the Gaon's name, a happy smile spread across his face. "For the Gaon of Vilna, I would be willing to part with this *esrog*," he declared. "But I ask for one thing in return."

The messengers had already decided to pay any price for this *esrog*, but still they were shocked at the merchant's next words: "I don't want to be paid in money for this *esrog*. Instead, I am requesting that the Gaon give me his reward for this year's mitzvah of the *arba'ah minim*."

The messengers felt they had no choice. They just couldn't return to the Gaon empty-handed. They agreed to the merchant's condition and took the *esrog*.

As they approached Vilna, they worried how the

Gaon would react when he would hear what they had promised in exchange for this *esrog*.

Finally the messengers arrived at the Gaon's home. They showed him the *esrog*, and the Gaon's entire face lit up. "It is beautiful!" he declared.

With pounding hearts, the oldest messenger in the group tried to tell the Gaon the "price" they had paid for this *esrog*. "Th-the merchant we bought this *esrog* from had a v-very unusual request…"

"Yes?" The Gaon smiled at him encouragingly.

"In exchange for this *esrog*, he asked that he receive the Gaon's reward for this mitzvah…"

The Gaon actually looked very pleased! "Of course I am willing to pay that price!" he exclaimed. "Have I not always hoped to perform at least one mitzvah without receiving reward for it? What a joy to fulfill the will of Hashem without expecting repayment!"

Indeed, all Yom Tov long, the Gaon seemed happier than usual each time he held his *arba'ah minim* in his hands!

CHAPTER SIX

The Greatness of the Gaon

O nce, on the first day of Chol Hamoed Sukkos, the Gaon's father discovered him sitting in his sukkah, looking happier than usual.

"Why are you so happy?" his father asked him.

The Gaon looked uncomfortable and didn't really want to explain. But his father insisted. "I command you to tell me."

The mitzvah of *kibbud av va'em* required that he respond, and so the Gaon said, "Yaakov Avinu was with me today in the sukkah…"

The Gaon was once sitting at a *seudah* during Pesach with two of his students, and they couldn't help noticing that he looked sad.

"What is wrong?" they asked. "Usually on Yom Tov you are so happy!" The Gaon did not want to reply, but his students didn't give up.

At last he told them. "I will reveal something that I would usually keep a secret, in order to fulfill the *pasuk, When a man has a worry in his heart, he should tell it to others* (Mishlei 12:25).

"Last night, I learned from Eliyahu Hanavi some awesome secrets regarding the Name of Hashem, which are revealed in the *pasuk, Go up through the south* (Bamidbar 13:17). When I awoke, I couldn't help thinking about what I had learned, before I had a chance to say *Birkas HaTorah*." The Gaon was of the opinion that one is forbidden to even think about words of Torah before saying *Birkas HaTorah*. "As a result, I was punished, and I immediately forgot the insights."

The Gaon's students consoled him, and they blessed him, "May Hashem return your loss to you."

Months later, someone remembered to ask

the Gaon if he had recovered the Torah thoughts that he had lost. The Gaon replied, "*Baruch Hashem* they were revealed to me a second time. There are a total of 6,620 ways to understand the Name of Hashem in that *pasuk*. With one of those explanations, I was able to understand the powers of all creatures and the purpose of every part of the human body."

When the Vilna Gaon needed to know something important, he would sometimes fast to the point where he would become ill, until a secret was revealed to him by Heaven.

One of the Gaon's students, Rav Shaul Katzenellenbogen, once noticed that as his *rebbi* slept, his face looked pained. When Rav Shaul pressed the Gaon for an explanation, he told him that he could not bear the suffering of the souls of the dead, particularly those of Jews he had known in their lifetimes, who came to him for help as he slept.

• • •

The Gaon's prayers were so inspiring that Jews would travel great distances in order to observe him *daven*, and they would be transformed by the experience. One *rav* related that when he prayed with the Gaon, he could feel his fear of Hashem increasing. Even after he went home, for as long as he lived he was moved by the memory of what he had seen.

The Gaon told his student Rav Chaim of Volozhin, "I was once shown from Heaven the greatness of prayer. I had spent twelve weeks trying to understand a statement in the Torah about Rosh Chodesh, but without success. Then, on the first day of Rosh Chodesh, while I was in the middle of Shacharis, like a bolt of lightning I received seven ways to answer my question! I stopped *davening* for a moment to arrange my thoughts, thinking that it would not be considered an interruption."

"That's what I would have done," Rav Chaim commented.

"It took about a quarter of a minute until I processed and arranged the answers in my mind, and then I continued *davening.* But unfortunately, after my prayers I could no longer remember any of the answers—not one! Then I began *Mussaf,* and while in the middle of that, the seven answers came into my mind again! I wasn't going to make the same mistake twice, so I ignored the answers and just continued *davening.*"

"What happened this time?"

The Gaon smiled brightly. "When I finished my prayers, they were still arranged clearly in my mind, true as ever and sweeter than honey."

• • •

One day the Gaon was walking by the river with a *rav* from the Vilna community. They were discussing the kashrus of various types of fish. "I know all the fish of the river, except for one particular kind," the Gaon said.

A thrashing in the water made them turn their heads. The other *rav* pointed. "That's the very fish you were talking about!"

The fish hovered at the surface of the water, allowing the Gaon to examine it. When he was done, the fish dove back into the water.

• • •

In the house of Reb Nosson, his wife and daughters were putting the finishing touches on their Erev Shabbos preparations. When Reb Nosson walked into the kitchen, he happened to glance at the chicken in the pot, and he noticed that one of the wings was discolored, which could be an indication that the chicken had been injured before it was slaughtered. This could make the chicken *treif*. Since it was late in the day, and he lived near the Gaon, Reb Nosson told his daughter Esther, "Please run to the Gaon and describe our chicken to him. Ask him if it is kosher."

Esther ran out, and her father hurried to the bathhouse to wash up for Shabbos. (In those days people had no bathtubs at home; they would take baths in the bathhouse instead.)

Reb Nosson's wife noticed the chicken moments later, and she too realized that they had a *she'eilah* on their hands. "Esther, Esther, please come here quickly!" she called to her eldest daughter.

"Esther is not here. Tatte sent her somewhere," Golda, the second daughter, told her mother.

"Then Golda, you will have to run to the *rav* and tell him that the wing of the chicken is discolored. Ask him what we should do."

Esther and Golda met on their way back. "Where were you?" Golda asked, as they walked home together.

"Tatte sent me to the Vilna Gaon to ask about the discolored wing."

"Oh, that's interesting," Golda said. "Mama sent me to the *rav* with the same question! So, what did the Gaon say?"

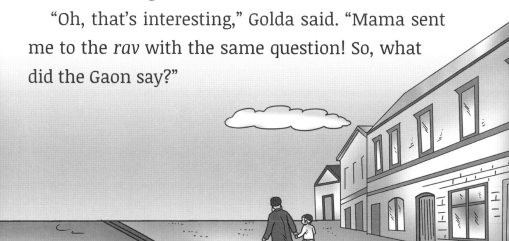

"That the chicken is *treif*, and we can't eat it."

Golda stopped in her tracks. "Now we are in trouble."

"Why?"

"Because the *rav* said the chicken is kosher!'"

When Reb Nosson heard about this, he did not know what to do. He decided to tell the *rav* what had happened. "There was some confusion," he said hesitantly. "I noticed the problem and sent my daughter to the Gaon. Unfortunately, I did not mention it to my wife. She also noticed the problem, and sent another daughter to you." He took a deep breath. "You said the chicken is fine, but the Gaon said that it's *treif*! Now what should I do?"

The *rav* replied, "Since I *paskened* that the chicken is kosher, go home and tell your wife that it can be cooked and eaten. Tonight, the Gaon and I will come to your house and have some of that chicken."

Reb Nosson hurried home to tell his wife about the extraordinary guests they would be having. At

the same time the *rav* was hurrying to the home of the Gaon.

"I am happy to see you," said the Gaon. "There must be something important that brings you here now, so close to Shabbos. How can I help you?"

The *rav* told him about the mix-up. "Rebbi, I know that I am like dust beneath your feet, but I am responsible for the kashrus decisions here in Vilna. In order to do my job properly, I need the *kehillah* to respect my *psak*. So I ask you to please come with me tonight to the house of Reb Nosson, and we will eat the chicken together. This will make it clear to everyone that I know what I am doing."

"Of course," the Gaon humbly replied.

During the Friday night *seudah*, the two came to Reb Nosson's home together. They sat down at the table, and Reb Nosson's wife brought in the pot of chicken.

Then something unexpected happened. There was a lamp with candles that hung over the table,

and one of the candles from it suddenly fell down, into the pot! Everyone gasped. In those days candles were made from tallow, a *treif* substance. Now the chicken for sure could not be eaten! Hashem had protected the Gaon from sinning even accidentally or unknowingly.

• • •

Someone once brought the Gaon beautiful *hadassim* for Sukkos. Joyfully he reached for the *hadassim*, but as soon as he examined them, he dropped them. "These *hadassim* cannot be used. They have been grafted (made out of two types of leaves grown together), and grafted plants cannot be used for the *arba'ah minim*."

The Gaon was very strict about not consuming food and drink that had been left under the bed of someone who was sleeping. At a *simchah* someone once brought the Gaon a glass of wine. He took the glass and then put it down. "One shouldn't drink

something that was under a sleeping person's bed," the Gaon explained. The host had not been aware that the wine had been stored under a bed by a family member.

He told a student who was helping him, "It is important to always bring me water from the well and never from the uncovered barrel." The young man was very careful to do just that, until one night during a terrible storm, when he just couldn't get himself to head to the well through the pouring rain in the pitch-black courtyard. Instead, he filled a pitcher from the barrel of water that stood right outside the house, and brought it to the Gaon.

The next morning the Gaon called to him in distress, "Why did you bring me uncovered water? I had a lot of trouble *davening* this morning. My prayers were disturbed by terrible images!"

• • •

One of the Gaon's students became blind. He continued to study by heart, and he became an

outstanding Torah scholar. The Gaon found a *shidduch* for him, and the girl's father promised to support the couple if he continued to learn Torah.

On the wedding day, the Gaon was filled with joy. His happiness was obvious to all the guests. When the *chassan* was brought to the bride to cover her face with a veil, the Gaon turned to the *chassan* and said, "Our Sages have said that a man may not marry a woman until he has had a chance to look at her!"

At that moment, light flooded the *chassan's* eyes. He could see again! He looked at the face of his bride, just as the Gaon instructed him.

•   •   •

On another occasion, a group of peasants from Zaretshe once set out to kill as many Jews as they could. From the window of the *beis midrash*, where he was learning, the Gaon could see the crowd of murderers surging onto the bridge that led to

the Jewish community. They were yelling terrible, hateful things.

The Gaon began to pray, "Guardian of Israel, save the remnant of Israel!"

With a terrible noise, the metal supports of the bridge suddenly broke! Most of the murderers fell into the water, while the rest of them wisely decided to run away. Once again, the holiness of the Gaon had protected the Jews' lives.

• • •

A lot of people lived long lives after receiving a *brachah* from the Gaon.

On Chol Hamoed many scholars would come to celebrate Yom Tov with the Gaon. A topic he often spoke about during these occasions was the importance of setting aside time to learn Torah.

One Sukkos, a man came into the Gaon's sukkah to speak to him. The Gaon was concentrating on his learning and didn't realize that he had a visitor.

The man was very hurt and sadly left the sukkah. "I don't understand how the Gaon could ignore me like that!" he complained to a friend.

The friend replied, "Let us go together to speak with the Gaon, and we will ask him if he has anything against you."

The Gaon was deeply distressed. "*Chas v'shalom!*" he replied. "Why should I be upset with a man who has come to join me in my happiness? May Hashem lengthen his days to a hundred years!"

Many years passed, and this person remained strong and healthy. When he was ninety-eight years old, he grew ill. His children and grandchildren wanted to call a doctor.

"There is no need for a doctor," the old man said. "The Gaon promised me one hundred years. I have two years and a few days left, and I expect to live for every one of them!" And so it was. The man lived his full one hundred years.

One day after *davening*, the Gaon was pacing

back and forth, immersed in his thoughts. There was a boy who had also prayed in that *minyan*, and he too was walking back and forth, saying Tehillim with great feeling. The child accidentally stepped on the *tzitzis* of the Gaon's *tallis*. When the Gaon turned toward him, the boy froze in his place, overwhelmed with awe.

The Gaon saw the boy's fright and confusion. He lovingly put his hand on the boy's shoulder and said, "May you live for a long time, my son, but please step off of my *tzitzis*."

When his father heard about the *brachah* that his son had received from the Gaon, he made a *seudah* to celebrate. This boy grew up to be a noted Torah scholar. In his old age, whenever someone would tell him to watch his health, he would say that he wasn't worried, because he had the protection of the Gaon's *brachah*. He lived in good health until almost ninety.

• • •

Rav Chaim Volozhiner was the Gaon's very close student. When he would mention the name of his great teacher, Rav Chaim would tremble, and his entire appearance would change.

Once, when Rav Chaim was preparing to visit the Gaon, his son Yitzchak, who was then a boy, said, "Father, I want to go as well."

"You want to go to the Gaon as well?" Rav Chaim repeated, trembling.

Yitzchak, too, grew frightened, but he said, "Yes, Father."

Rav Chaim hesitated, but in the end he agreed to take his son along. As they rode on the wagon to Vilna, Yitzchak looked at his father and saw that he was terribly pale. The closer they got to Vilna, the paler Rav Chaim became, and by the time they entered Vilna, Yitzchak found it difficult to recognize his father. When they stood outside the Gaon's door, Rav Chaim was shaking so violently that his knees knocked against each other!

After the Gaon's *petirah*, when people called Rav Chaim "the Vilna Gaon's *talmid*," he would say, "I know only a fraction of what he knew. I did not come near his great mastery over every single detail of the Torah. He understood everything so clearly, in a way that no one else could."

CHAPTER SEVEN

Eretz Yisrael

Because he loved the mitzvos so much, the Vilna Gaon wanted badly to go to Eretz Yisrael, since there are many mitzvos that can only be kept there. At one point he made up his mind that he would travel there. No one in Vilna wanted to let the Gaon go, because they loved him so much. But of course, they would not try to stop him. Instead they brought him money to hire wagons and horses for his journey and to pay the captain of a ship to take him across the sea.

The Gaon's bags were carried to the wagon that stood waiting at the door of his house. "When I get to Eretz Yisrael, I will send for you," he told his

family. After saying goodbye, the Gaon climbed into the wagon, and the driver drove off. All along the streets of the city, the people stood calling out, "*L'chaim u'l'shalom*! Go in life and peace!" Tears fell from many eyes as he passed. The Jews of Vilna were certain that they would never see the Gaon again.

The wagon left the city, and the long journey began.

One night, while still in the midst of traveling, the Gaon sat down to write a letter to a certain Jew by the name of Rav Leib. He gave it to a messenger to deliver for him in Rav Leib's village. When the messenger entered the small village, he stopped a Jew on the street and told him, "I have a letter for Rav Leib."

"Rav Leib?" the man repeated. "Maybe you have the wrong village. There is no Rav Leib here."

"It can't be," insisted the messenger. "The man who sent me here would not make a mistake like that."

"Maybe he means Leibele from the vodka factory?"

Since there was no other Leib in the village, the messenger headed to the vodka factory. When he got there, he told the owner, "I am looking for Rav Leibele."

The owner burst out laughing. "There is no Rav Leibele here, only Leibele the vodka maker!"

"All right," said the messenger. "Maybe he is the one I am looking for."

"What do you want to talk to him about?" the owner asked.

"It's private."

The owner shrugged his shoulders and pointed to a large building behind him. "You will find him near the oven."

When the messenger entered the building, he saw a simple-looking man sitting next to the blazing oven, reciting Tehillim.

"I have a letter for you from the Vilna Gaon."

The man did not look surprised. He took the letter, read it, and then threw it into the fire.

"Do you have anything to say in response to the Gaon?" the messenger asked.

"Tell him that it isn't necessary."

"What isn't necessary?"

But Leibele would say no more, so the messenger left.

Leibele was still sitting next to the oven, reciting Tehillim, when his boss walked in.

"Leibele, I want you to tell me what was written in the letter you just received."

Leibele continued saying Tehillim and did not respond.

"If you won't tell me what was in that letter," the owner declared, "I will fire you, and you won't have a job anymore."

Finally Leibele spoke up. "The Vilna Gaon wanted me to travel with him to Eretz Yisrael. But I said that I don't have to go with him, for he too will return without having gone there."

Rav Leibele's words turned out to be true. The Gaon crossed the border of Lithuania, and soon enough entered the country of Hungary. From there he sent a letter to his family telling them that he was well, and offering precious advice regarding how to be righteous and grow in Torah.

But then suddenly one day, the Gaon returned home! He never explained why he came back. When he was asked, he just sighed and said, "I was prevented by Heaven from reaching Eretz Yisrael."

The rich men of Vilna who had given the Gaon money for his journey did not expect him to return the money. They understood that there had been many expenses for the journey, and that he had used the money to pay for wagons and places to stay. But the Gaon made sure to return every last penny.

Once the Gaon was back in Vilna, he continued to learn Torah in the same way as he had always done. More and more *rabbanim* came to him with questions about things they couldn't understand. There was never a question that he couldn't answer. He didn't need to look up anything; he seemed to remember everything he had ever learned! Yet even though he knew so much, he still kept learning Torah, as intensely as ever, for the Torah is like an ocean without a bottom. You can always dive deeper into it, and discover more and more pearls.

CHAPTER EIGHT
The Gaon's Last Years

The Gaon became older. Although his hair and beard had turned white, his eyes still shone brightly, and his skin remained clear and smooth. He had no wrinkles except for the deep ones on his forehead. In the year 1791, when he was seventy years old, he became ill. The news spread quickly through the city. "The Gaon is not well!" Everyone said Tehillim, begging Hashem that their *rav* should become strong again. Hashem helped, and their prayers were answered.

The next year, the city of Vilna came under attack. For a very long time the countries of Lithuania (where Vilna is) and Poland were united into one kingdom. Now the mighty Queen Catherine of Russia sent her army to conquer part of that kingdom for herself. The Russian soldiers were stronger than the Polish soldiers. When the Russian soldiers got to Vilna, they surrounded the city, set up their cannons, and began firing at the houses.

Two messengers ran to the Gaon's house. "Rebbi! Rebbi!" they cried. "We are in danger! Come and pray for us. We are all waiting for you in the large shul."

The aged Gaon rose slowly. He closed his Gemara and went with the two messengers. Stepping outside, they could hear the loud booms of the cannons. As they approached the shul, weeping could be heard.

When the Gaon entered, everyone rose. Slowly he walked through the rows of pale, frightened faces, and up the steps leading to the *aron kodesh*. He opened the *aron kodesh* and began to recite Chapter 20 from Tehillim.

Hashem will answer you on the day of distress… Everyone repeated after him.

Suddenly there was a terrible THUD on the rooftop! The walls of the shul shook. Frightened screams filled the air. The hearts of those *davening* almost stopped beating. The Gaon could be heard calling out, "*Batel, batel*—I am ordering the cannon not to explode!"

After a moment, the Gaon said, "Everyone can calm down. We have been saved. Our prayers have been answered."

And so it was. The Poles opened the gates of the city and surrendered to the Russians, and soon Vilna was at peace once again, although it was now under Russian rule.

When everything had settled down, some men climbed to the rooftop of the shul to see what had fallen there. They found a huge cannonball which, miraculously, had not done any damage!

For many years after this event occurred, the Jews of Vilna would commemorate the miracle by saying special *tefillos* in shul on this day. They

kept the cannonball exactly where it had fallen, on the rooftop of the shul, and it remained there for about 150 years, until the shul was destroyed by the Nazis during World War II.

• • •

The Gaon never revealed certain secrets of the Torah. "I am saving these words of Torah for the World to Come," he would say. "When a person arrives at the Heavenly Yeshivah, the tzaddikim there wish to hear insights on the Torah that he taught, and the person is given one hundred and eighty days to speak of what he has learned," he explained.

In 1796 the Gaon fell ill again. This time it was more serious, but he did not want to go to a doctor. "I have never gone to a doctor or taken medicine in my entire life," he said. "I do not wish to start now." He was so connected to the Doctor of all doctors—Hashem— that on his level, he truly needed nothing else.

But seeing how weak the Gaon was, the members of his family insisted that a doctor be called, and the Gaon gave in.

Dr. Yaakov Lubavitch was sent for. When he put his ear to the Gaon's chest, he heard the Gaon murmuring a mishnah. When he came out of the room, the family asked, "Where is he holding?" They wanted to know how he was doing, but Dr. Lubavitch smiled and said, "He is holding in the middle of the Gemara *Keilim*." The Gaon didn't stop learning just because he was ill.

Rosh Hashanah arrived. Because the Gaon was so weak and unwell, the doctor declared that he could not fast on Yom Kippur. The Gaon, who knew more about medicine than trained doctors, sat up in his bed. "Doctor, how many muscles did I use when I just sat up?"

"I don't know," the doctor said.

"When you are more knowledgeable, I will listen to your prescriptions," the Gaon replied. He knew

that fasting on Yom Kippur would not endanger his health any further.

On Erev Yom Kippur, the Gaon called all his family and students to his bedside and blessed them. That Yom Kippur, a *minyan davened* right outside the Gaon's room. He did not have the strength to *daven* all the *tefillos* with the *minyan*, but he kept the door of his room open, and came out to the *minyan* for *Shemoneh Esrei* and the reading of the Torah.

With each passing day, he grew weaker. Two days before Sukkos, Reb Shmuel Yudes brought the Gaon a beautiful *esrog*. He expected the Gaon to smile and warmly thank him, as he did every year, but when the Gaon saw the *esrog*, he turned his face to the wall and began to cry. Everyone in the room was shocked. Why was the Gaon crying? It wouldn't become clear until later.

By Erev Sukkos, the Gaon could no longer get out of his bed. He asked that his bed be moved into the sukkah.

The whole city was very worried. People kept coming to the Gaon's house to ask how he was doing. When two people met in the street, one would ask the other, "How is the Gaon feeling? Have you heard anything?" The people tried to be happy, because it was Sukkos, but no one could forget that the beloved Vilna Gaon was very, very ill.

On the third day of Chol Hamoed, the Gaon took his *lulav* and *esrog* early in the morning and recited the *brachah* over it, with great joy. It was his custom to carry around the *arba'ah minim* all day long, so he held them close to him all throughout the day.

Then he took his *tzitzis* in his hand and, with tears pouring from his eyes, he said, "World, world, how fine you are, how beautiful you are! How hard it is to leave such a world! Here, with such an easy mitzvah, which costs only a few coins, a person can rise to stand before Hashem's presence. But in the World to Come, a person cannot get such things, even if he gives all of his strength for it!"

The Gaon asked for a glass of wine to make a *brachah* on and to drink. "My whole life, I gave my body very little," he said. "Now I wish to make peace with my body."

Later that morning, the holy soul of the Gaon slipped away from his body and returned to its Maker.

As the townspeople heard the sad news, the streets became filled with crying men, women, and children. Reb Shmuel Yudes, the man who had brought the *esrog* to the Gaon, now understood why the Gaon had cried when he'd handed the *esrog* to him. Shaking the *lulav* and *esrog* had been the last mitzvah *d'Oraisa* that the Gaon had performed while in This World.

The governor of Vilna sent seven soldiers to guard the *aron* of the Gaon. There was a *levayah*, but because it was Chol Hamoed, there were no *hespedim*. All over the world, wherever Jews lived, people spoke of the Gaon's greatness as they mourned his death.

After the Vilna Gaon's death, his outstanding students, who were great *rabbanim*, continued to spread the wisdom of the Vilna Gaon in their own *sefarim* and through their teachings. Rav Chaim of Volozhin, an especially devoted *talmid* of the Vilna Gaon, started a yeshivah in Volozhin modeled after the teachings of his *rebbi*. The renowned yeshivah stood for ninety years, and generations of *rabbanim* and *talmidei chachamim* learned there.

Rav Chaim impressed upon his students the greatness of the Gaon, telling them story after story about his devotion to Torah study. Many of Rav Chaim's *talmidim* started their own yeshivos, where they too related these incredible stories of Torah knowledge and learning that was beyond comparison.

Their students opened additional yeshivos, where the life of the Gaon and his writings would continue to serve as a source of inspiration to generations of Jewish students, until our own days.

ALSO FROM THE

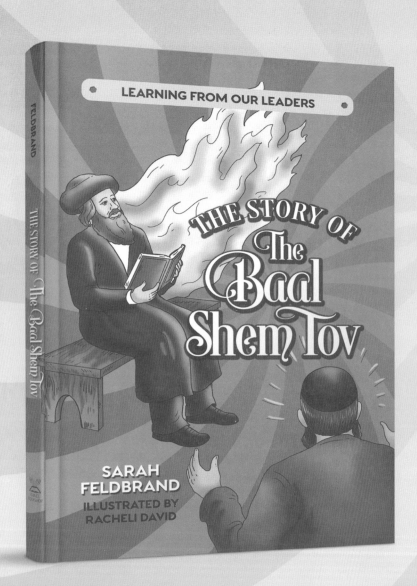

LEARNING FROM OUR LEADERS

THE STORY OF
The
Baal
Shem Tov

SARAH
FELDBRAND

ILLUSTRATED BY
RACHELI DAVID

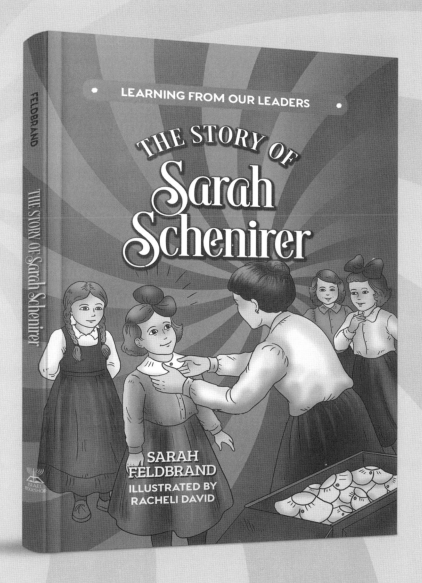

LEARNING FROM OUR LEADERS

THE STORY OF
Sarah Schenirer

SARAH
FELDBRAND

ILLUSTRATED BY
RACHELI DAVID

FELDBRAND

THE STORY OF Sarah Schenirer

ALSO FROM THE

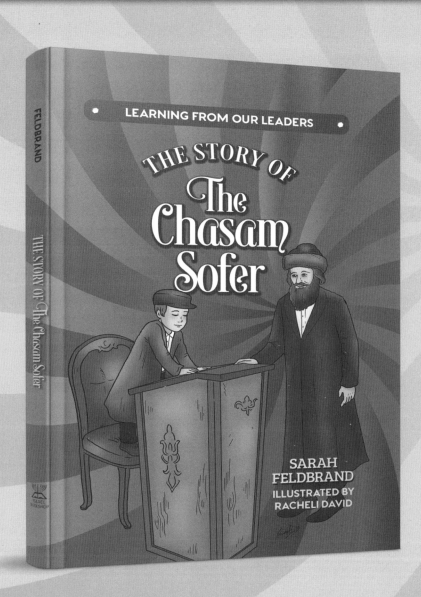

LEARNING FROM OUR LEADERS

THE STORY OF
The Chasam Sofer

SARAH FELDBRAND
ILLUSTRATED BY
RACHELI DAVID

FELDBRAND

THE STORY OF The Chasam Sofer

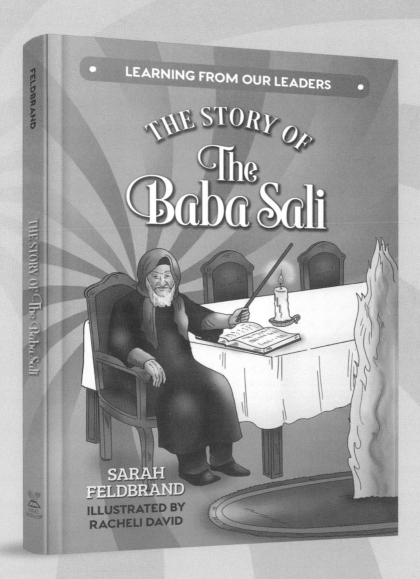

LEARNING FROM OUR LEADERS

THE STORY OF

The Baba Sali

SARAH
FELDBRAND

ILLUSTRATED BY
RACHELI DAVID

FELDBRAND

THE STORY OF The Baba Sali

ALSO FROM THE

LEARNING FROM OUR LEADERS

SERIES

LEARNING FROM OUR LEADERS

THE STORY OF
The
Ribnitzer
Rebbe

SARAH
FELDBRAND

ILLUSTRATED BY
RACHELI DAVID

FELDBRAND

THE STORY OF The Ribnitzer Rebbe